Book 19—Gospels

The Early Years of Jesus

Written by Anne de Graaf

Illustrated by José Pérez Montero

Family Time Bible Stories

Standard Publishing

Gospels-The Early Years of Jesus

Isaiah 9:11, 12; Luke 1-5; Matthew 1-4, 14; Psalm 139; Micah 5; Mark 1, 6; John 1-2

About the New Testament

The Old Testament tells the story of God's people. It is a story that leads from the creation of the world directly to Jesus.

The Jewish people living at the time Jesus was born knew their history. They knew of Abraham who left his homeland in obedience to God. They knew that God had chosen Moses to lead their ancestors to the promised land. And they knew about their judges, priests, and the great king, David.

They also knew that God had promised them a Savior, a Messiah. The promise had been given to Abraham. "In you," God told Abraham, "all the families of the world will be blessed."

Moses knew of God's promise of a Messiah. So did David. And the prophets said many things about this Savior. "He'll be a king in David's line," they said. "A man acquainted with sorrows." "From Bethlehem," Micah said, "will come the ruler of Israel."

At the time of Jesus' birth, many Jews were ready for Him to come.

About the Four Gospels:
Matthew, Mark, Luke and John

The four Gospels tell us about Jesus. They tell us He was born in a tiny town of parents who were not rich or famous or well-educated. He lived in a province that was ruled by Rome. Jesus only lived on earth 33 years. Then He was killed on the cross as a traitor.

Jesus did not know the important people of His time. He was hated by many of the leaders in Palestine. Yet, Jesus' life has changed the life of millions.

The Gospels tell us about Jesus' miracles and teaching. But they also tell us that He came to offer salvation and a personal relationship with God.

THE PROMISED KING

To Wait and Pray

Isaiah 11:1—12:6; Luke 1:1-4

The Jews knew that someday God would send the Messiah to save them. Messiah means "one who brings God close to us." Jesus does this. He is also called "Savior" and "Anointed One." This last name means He has the power of God with Him.

God helped the prophet Isaiah look into the future many hundreds of years before Jesus was born. Isaiah wrote that Jesus would belong to the family of David. He wrote that Jesus would be wise and understanding, yet also strong and able to know who is good and who is evil.

What Isaiah predicted came true. Luke wrote about it in a letter to a friend. Luke was very careful to write things down exactly as they happened. He wanted people to know the truth about Jesus, no matter how many years had gone by. We call Luke's letter "The Gospel of Luke." Gospel means "good news." To write his Gospel, Luke must have talked with Mark, Jesus' mother, Mary, and many others who knew Jesus well.

God Promises a Baby

Luke 1:5-22

In the time just before Jesus was born, there was an old priest named Zacharias. He and his wife Elizabeth had wanted a baby for many, many years. But as they grew older, no children came.

One day, Zacharias went into the temple alone to burn incense to God. While he stood there alone, an angel appeared. Zacharias was afraid. He had never seen an angel before!

"Don't be frightened, Zacharias," the angel said. "God has heard your prayers. Elizabeth will have a baby, and you will name him John. He will be filled with the Holy Spirit, and God will use him in a special way. He will speak God's own words as he helps the people get ready for the Messiah."

Zacharias just could not believe that his wife, who was so old, would be able to have a child. So he asked the angel for a sign, something that would prove the angel was telling the truth.

But the angel said, "I am Gabriel, who stands in the presence of God. Because you do not believe me, you will not be able to speak until the baby is born."

When Zacharias went outside, he could not talk. No one could understand what had happened to him.

Zacharias went home. And soon afterwards, just as Gabriel had predicted, Elizabeth became pregnant. She would have a baby after all!

5

An Angel Visits a Young Girl

Luke 1:26-38

Mary woke up and sat in her bed. A bright light streamed in her room, and she knew it was not the sun.

The angel Gabriel, the same angel who had appeared to Zacharias six months earlier, entered Mary's room. "Greetings, Mary! You are very special to God!"

Mary was a little bit scared. Why was the angel in her room? And what could he possibly mean?

"Do not be afraid, Mary. You have been chosen by God to be the mother of His Son Jesus, the Messiah who will have a never-ending kingdom."

Mary was probably about fifteen years old. It was not unusual then for girls to be engaged at that age, and Mary was going to marry a man named

Joseph. She heard the angel's words and thought to herself, "Any girl who is going to have a baby and is not married will have a lot of trouble." She knew Joseph would no longer want to marry her if she was going to have a baby.

But instead of arguing with the angel or doubting what he said as Zacharias had, Mary accepted the angel's words. She knew God loved her and would take care of her.

God would cause His very own Son to grow inside Mary, and be born. Baby Jesus would become a little boy and grow up to be a man. He would still stay just as perfect as He was when He lived in Heaven with God.

When Gabriel told Mary that her relative Elizabeth was also going to have a baby, he added, "Nothing is impossible with God."

And Mary believed him.

A Trip Over the Mountains

Luke 1:39-56

Soon afterwards Mary left her home in Nazareth and traveled to Judea to visit Elizabeth. As she crossed the hills, she wondered why God had chosen her to be the mother of His Son. He was so great and she was just an ordinary girl.

Mary did not understand it. But she was excited. She had chosen to accept God's plan, and even though she might not know how everything would work out, Mary did know God was in control. That was all that mattered.

When Mary arrived at the home of Elizabeth and Zacharias, she called out, "Hello, Elizabeth!"

7

At the sound of Mary's voice, Elizabeth came running. She cried, "Mary, you are blessed by God! You are the mother of my Lord! I know this because when you called out, my own baby jumped for joy inside me. You are very special indeed, because God's Son lives in you."

Knowing that Elizabeth shared her special secret, Mary felt so happy she wanted to sing.

"My soul is so happy," she sang. "God is so great. He makes mighty rulers fall. He saves the poor and humble. He has remembered His people and the promise He made to them so long ago. He will help Israel again!"

Mary stayed with Elizabeth for three months, until Elizabeth's baby was almost due to be born.

"My Son Is Called John!"

Luke 1:57-80

Now all this time, poor old Zacharias had not been able to talk because he had not believed the angel Gabriel.

The day finally came for Elizabeth to have her baby. It was a little boy with sparkling dark eyes. All the neighbors and family were so happy for Elizabeth and Zacharias.

When the boy was eight days old, it was time to give him a name. In those days most people named a son after his father, but Elizabeth said, "No, his name is John."

"What's this?" the crowd murmured. "There is no one in the family with that name. Why would she want to call the baby John?" But just to make sure, they asked Zacharias what he thought.

And because he could not talk, he wrote down on a tablet, "His name is John." They were all astonished.

But what was even more astonishing was that the minute Zacharias finished writing the note, he opened his mouth and could talk again! The first thing he said was how great God is. He thanked God for his son, who would grow into a prophet of God. John would prepare the way for the Messiah, the one who would come and save God's people from themselves.

But the people who heard Zacharias were afraid. They could see that God was watching over the baby boy, and they wondered what kind of man he would become.

Beside the Well

Matthew 1:1-19

When Mary returned to Nazareth after visiting Elizabeth, she knew she would soon have to tell Joseph about the baby inside her. She prayed that God would prepare him for the news.

"Joseph," she said, "something has happened that is hard to believe, but true. You know how our fathers and their fathers have been waiting for so many years, hoping the Promised One would come to deliver Israel? He was to be born in your family, descended from the throne of David."

Joseph nodded. He wondered why Mary looked so serious.

"Well," Mary continued, "God has blessed me very much. I don't know why, but He has chosen me to be the mother of the Messiah, His Son. The baby inside me is already three months old.

"Oh, Mary..." Joseph turned away from her. "I love her so much," he thought. "But I cannot take her as my wife now." Her story sounded too amazing, as if she had made it up.

He looked back at her again. Mary's eyes shone with confidence, yet he just could

not believe such a wild story. Joseph walked away, trying to think of ways he could call off the wedding without hurting Mary too much.

Joseph's Dream

Matthew 1:20-24; Psalm 139:1-18

One night soon afterwards, an angel of the Lord appeared to Joseph in a dream. "Son of David, do not be afraid to make Mary your wife. She speaks the truth. The Son she will bear is the one who will save His people from their sins. You will call Him Jesus."

When Joseph woke up, he came to Mary and said everything was all right. A short time later, he and Mary were married.

Mary and Joseph spent the next few months waiting together for the birth of Jesus. They often thought about and prayed for the baby inside Mary, whom God was making.

Joseph's ancestor, King David, had written long ago that the Lord knows us inside and out. God understands even those things we puzzle over. When a baby grows inside his mother, God knows and loves that baby, weaving the parts together. King David said there is no place far enough or dark enough where we can hide from God's love.

There in the tiny village of Nazareth, God was making His Son grow inside Mary. And soon the Savior would be born.

GOD KEEPS HIS PROMISE

Jesus Is Born

Matthew 1:25; Isaiah 9:1-7; Micah 5:1-6; Luke 2:1-7

It was very early in the morning. The sun had not yet risen. Joseph leaned over Mary and shook her softly. "It is time to go, Mary. Wake up."

Joseph had waited until the last possible moment. The donkey was packed. They had a long journey ahead of them and needed an early start.

Mary opened her eyes. "Yes, I'm coming," she said. She was ready in a few moments. Then she climbed on the donkey.

Joseph and Mary were going to Bethlehem. The emperor, Caesar Augustus, had told everyone to go back to the town where his family was from, so his soldiers could count the number of people in the tribes of Israel.

Joseph's family came from Bethlehem, so that was where he had to go, together with Mary.

The hours passed. When the sun rose, it became hot. Mary wanted to fall asleep, but she knew she would fall off if she did. She walked for a little while,

but she soon became so tired that Joseph put her back on the donkey.

Finally they arrived in Bethlehem. The streets were crowded. There seemed to be children running everywhere, and so much noise! Mary wanted to cover her ears. Suddenly, she felt a tightening in her abdomen. She knew what it meant. "Joseph, the baby! I think the baby will be born soon."

"We have to get you somewhere quiet, out of all this crowd," he said.

"Go behind the town," someone told Joseph. "There is a hillside near the pastures. In the hillside is a deep cave where the animals stay in bad weather. Take Mary to the cave and lay down some fresh hay. It is my property and no one will bother you. At least it is quiet."

Joseph shouted his thanks over his shoulder. Mary leaned on him as the two made their way out of town to the hillside.

Once Mary was safe in the cave, Joseph relaxed. He had been praying so hard that all would go well.

It was a long night. While the baby was being born, Joseph helped Mary in every way he could. Finally, Joseph held the tiny baby boy in his arms. He gave the little one to Mary. She looked up at Joseph with happy tears in her eyes and said, "This is Jesus."

The Shepherds

Luke 2:8-17

While Mary and Joseph took care of baby Jesus that night, a strange thing happened in the nearby hills. A group of shepherds were keeping watch over their sheep. Suddenly the sky was filled with light, and the shepherds saw an angel standing in front of them. "Do not be afraid," the angel said. "A Savior has been born tonight. You will know it is true when you see a baby wrapped in clothes and lying in a manger."

Then there were angels all around. They praised God, saying, "Glory to God in the highest, and on earth peace to men who please Him."

When the angels left and it was dark again, the shepherds looked at each other in amazement.

They hurried toward town to find the new born baby. The shepherds told Mary and Joseph what the angels had said. Then they left, praising God for all they had seen and heard.

An Old Man's Wish Comes True

Luke 2:22-38

When baby Jesus was forty days old, His parents brought Him to the temple, according to Jewish law. Mary and Joseph planned to offer two doves as a sacrifice to God. This was also one of the rules God had given to Moses, so long ago.

In the temple courts, Mary and Joseph saw a very old man watching them. He was staring at the baby. Mary smiled at him and the old man came closer.

He reached out a hand to touch the little head of Jesus. Then, very softly, he took the baby from Mary and cuddled Him. "I bless You, Lord," he said. "Now I have seen Your salvation, the light that will save both the Jews and the non-Jews."

Joseph and Mary were amazed at what they heard the old man, Simeon, say. Simeon told them how God had promised he would not die until he had seen the Messiah. The Spirit of God had told Simeon that the Savior would be at the temple that day.

"This is He," he said. "Because of Jesus many people will change their ways of thinking. Even you," he looked at Mary, "will feel like a sword has cut open your soul after you see and hear all that He has come here to do."

Then an old woman came toward the little group. Her name was Anna and she was blessed by God, able to speak about things that had not yet happened.

Anna's husband had died when they were married for only seven years. Since then she had lived in the temple, serving God and praying to Him.

Anna looked down at the little baby and said, "Thank You, God. This is the one we have waited so long for. He will save Israel."

Mary and Joseph finished their sacrifice of the two doves. Then Mary turned to Joseph with tears in her eyes. So many wonderful things had happened since they had come to Bethlehem. Joseph held her in his arms. "God is in control," he whispered. And Mary nodded.

The Star and the Wisemen

Matthew 2:1-10

Visitors! Baby Jesus was going to have visitors. But these were no ordinary visitors. They were three wisemen from faraway lands in the east. They had seen a bright star in the night skies and traveled a long distance to Jerusalem. "Where is the one born king of the Jews?" We have come to worship Him."

King Herod called the Jewish leaders. "Where is the king of the Jews supposed to be born?" he asked.

"In Bethlehem," they answered. They knew the answer because that was what the prophet had written many years earlier.

16

"When did the star appear?" Herod asked the wisemen. They told him. Then Herod told the wisemen to go to Bethlehem. "And when you have found the child, come tell me, so I can worship Him.."

The wisemen went on to Bethlehem. They followed the star until it stopped over the house where Mary, Joseph, and the baby now lived. When they went into the house and saw baby Jesus, they smiled and laughed. Their long journey had been worth it. They had found the king!

Gifts for a King

Matthew 2:11-12

The three men unloaded their camels and brought in rare and beautiful gifts. Mary and Joseph's eyes grew round.

One of the wisemen bowed. "We have traveled a long way, knowing a great king of the Jews was to be born soon. The star showed us where to go. It is your Son we have come to see. Here is gold for a great king." He laid the gold at Jesus feet.

"It does not happen often that such a large star would be in the skies, the second wiseman said. This baby will be the greatest of all men." He laid a jar of myrrh at Jesus' feet. Myrrh is perfume that could only be worn by very important men.

The third wiseman smiled at Mary and Joseph. "This is incense for burning," he said. "It will make the air sweet. Incense is pleasing to God. We don't know how, but this king is both man and God." He bowed down and backed away.

God warned the wisemen not to go back to see King Herod, and they went home a different way than they had come.

Flight to Egypt

Matthew 2:13-18

After the wisemen left, Joseph had a dream. An angel of the Lord said, "Take the child and His mother and run away to Egypt. Stay there until I tell you. Herod is going to look for the child, to kill Him."

Joseph woke Mary up and told her about the dream. They quickly packed up their few things and put them on the donkey. Joseph gently lifted the

17

sleeping Jesus and put Him into Mary's arms. He led the donkey away from the house and disappeared into the dark night.

Meanwhile, King Herod had waited and waited for the three wisemen to return from their visit. When they did not show up, he grew angry. He had wanted to trick them, but they had tricked him instead.

"They were to tell me where this king of the Jews is. And now they are gone and I do not know!" he yelled.

Herod did not like the idea of another king. He wanted to be the only king.

"Whoever this king of the Jews is, I will kill Him! I may not know where He is, but I know He is still just a baby!"

Herod ordered a terrible thing. He told his soldiers to go out into

Bethlehem, and kill every baby boy they could find. No matter how much the mothers and fathers cried and begged, the soldiers would not spare the children. They tramped in and out of homes, looking for baby boys. But when they came to the house where Mary and Joseph and baby Jesus had lived, it was empty. The little family was safe, and on their way to Egypt.

JESUS GROWS UP

"He Will Be Called a Nazarene"

Matthew 2:19-23; Luke 2:39

Several years passed and the wicked King Herod finally died. Joseph had led Mary and Jesus safely to Egypt and they lived there, waiting for word from God that they could return to Israel.

One night, an angel of the Lord again appeared to Joseph in a dream. "Wake up and take the child and His mother back to Israel," the angel said.

The next morning Joseph told Mary the good news. Soon they were on their way back home. But when they arrived in the part of Israel called Judea, they heard Herod's son was in power. Everyone said he was just as bad and cruel as his father had been. So Joseph moved his little family to another part of Israel, called Galilee.

Mary and Joseph settled in a village called Nazareth. There, in the springtime the flowers cover the hills with color. A long, long time ago, one of the prophets had said the Messiah

would be called a Nazarene. When Joseph chose to live in Nazareth, he made that prophecy come true.

In Nazareth Joseph set up shop as a carpenter. People came to him with their broken chairs and tables. Joseph sawed and hammered all day, carving wood into furniture. As Jesus grew into a boy, He often came in the shop to watch. When Joseph asked for help, Jesus would hand him tools.

In the evenings Joseph and Mary taught Jesus the Jewish history, and about loving God. But all along, Joseph and Mary had the feeling their little boy already knew a great deal about God. They learned from each other in those early years when Jesus was a boy.

Found in the Temple

Luke 2:41-52

When Jesus was twelve years old, Mary and Joseph took Him to Jerusalem for the Passover feast. The city was full of people, donkeys and camels.

When the festival was over, Mary and Joseph left to go home. They both thought Jesus was in another part of the group from Nazareth.

After a day of traveling, they looked for Him among their friends and relatives. But He wasn't there.

Mary and Joseph looked at each other, afraid. Jesus was still back in Jerusalem! How would they ever find Him? They hurried back to the city. For three days they searched for Him. They saw many children, but none of them was Jesus.

Mary and Joseph felt desperate. Finally, they went to the temple, where the Jewish people worshipped. There they saw a little group of Jewish teachers, sitting together and talking, and in the middle of the group was Jesus. He was talking too, and those who listened looked very interested in what He said.

Mary and Joseph were amazed. "We have looked everywhere for You," Mary said, "and we have been very worried."

Jesus said, "Why didn't you know where to look? Of course, the only place I could be is my Father's house."

Because Jesus was God's Son, the temple was His Father's house. But Mary and Joseph did not understand what Jesus meant. As they left the temple with Jesus, they heard people say, "How is it that such a young boy could have talked about the things He did with such understanding? He is more than clever; He is blessed with wisdom."

Jesus returned with His parents to Nazareth. He was a good boy and did what His parents told Him. His parents loved Him a great deal, and other people liked Him too. The older Jesus became, the more He seemed to understand about the ways of men and God. Mary watched Him and wondered all the time at how God's blessing was on His Son.

JOHN BAPTIZES THE PEOPLE

"Say You're Sorry!"

Matthew 3:1-12; Mark 1:1-8; Luke 3:1-18

Jesus had a cousin. He was the man the people called John the Baptist. John was the son of Elizabeth, Mary's relative. When Mary was pregnant with Jesus, she had gone to visit Elizabeth, and Elizabeth's baby had jumped inside her when Mary called hello. That baby was John the Baptist.

When John grew to be a man, he

went off by himself into the desert. God gave John a message there and told him to tell the people what He said.

When John came out of the desert, he was dressed in a camel-hair cloak and leather belt. John was used to eating insects and honey.

"Get ready!" he called out to the people. "Get ready for the One who is coming! He will choose between those who live good lives and those who live bad lives!"

"What should we do to get ready?" the people asked.

"Search your hearts and turn away from all the wrong things you have ever done! Start doing right!"

The people did as John said, for they believed him. They said they were sorry for their sins, and then John had them come down into the river. They waded out to him, then knelt, letting the water wash over them. As they came up out of the water, it was an outward sign of how God's forgiveness washes people clean from their sins, the wrong things they have done. These people were starting their lives over, promising to follow God.

Some people thought John might be the Messiah God had promised to send. But John said, "Someday there will be One who comes to make you clean on the inside. I baptize with water, but He will baptize with the Holy Spirit," John said.

The Holy Spirit is the part of God that helps people live as God wants them to. John meant that when Jesus baptized with God's Spirit, God's forgiveness would cover them, just as the water had.

The people wondered who John could be talking about. Would it be another great prophet, or could it be the Messiah?

Jesus Is Baptized

Matthew 3:13-17; Mark 1:9-11; Luke 3:21-22

Hundreds of people lined up to be baptized by John in the river. The crowds sat listening to him. Over and over, he said to the people coming to him, "Show that you're sorry. The kingdom of God is coming soon. Live a new life. Do not cheat or hurt people."

John looked up to see who was next in line. His eyes caught those of Jesus, standing on the shore. The two cousins stared at each other.

Jesus said, "Baptize me, John."

"I should be the one baptized by You," John said. "Why do You come to me?"

"It is important that you baptize me," Jesus said. Jesus did not need to be forgiven for doing wrong things. But because He is God's Son, it was right for Him to do all that God commanded. He was teaching by example what it means to be a servant of the Lord.

John bowed his head. He, too, would obey. The crowd watched, not understanding all that happened. Jesus went down into the water. When He came up, He was praying. Suddenly, it seemed like the sky split in two! God's Holy Spirit, taking the form of a dove,

came down and lighted on Jesus. A great voice spoke from the sky, "You are my Son. I have always loved You. You have always pleased Me." It was the voice of God, telling the people they should listen to Jesus.

Jesus and His Friend

John 1:19-34

John said, "I am not the Christ." John knew Jesus was the Messiah, or the Christ.

"Are you Elijah then, or the Prophet?"

"No," he answered.

The messengers grew angry. "Well, who are you then?"

"I am the voice of one crying in the wilderness. I have come to make the people ready to see the way of the Lord."

"But why are you baptizing then, if you are not the Christ or a prophet?"

"I baptize in water, but there is One who comes after me I am not even worthy to unbuckle His sandal."

A few days later John saw Jesus in the crowd. He called out, "There is the Lamb of God, who takes away the sin of the world! I have baptized in water so the people would know Him. The Spirit of God is with Him. This is the Son of God!"

When the Pharisees heard John, they grew even more confused and angry. They watched Jesus move through the crowd. "It is bad enough that John has so many people following him. But if this Jesus becomes even more popular than John, our problems are bigger than we think."

JESUS SAVES HIMSELF
The Devil Against Jesus

Matthew 4:1-12, 14:3-5; Mark 1:12-14, 6:17-20; Luke 3:19, 20, 4:1-13

After Jesus was baptized in the river, He went into the desert, led by the

Holy Spirit. There He was tempted by Satan.

Satan wanted to spoil God's plans for Jesus. He wanted Jesus to choose to use His power for bad, instead of good.

Jesus was in the desert for forty days and nights. Satan knew Jesus had not eaten all that time, so he first tried to tempt Jesus with food. "If You are the Son of God, tell this stone to become bread." That would mean that Jesus would rather take care of himself than obey God.

But Jesus answered that the Scriptures said that man shall not live on bread alone, but also on God's Word.

Then Satan led Jesus to the top of a high place. "If You are the Son of God," he said "throw yourself down. You won't get hurt. God's angels will help you."

Jesus replied, "The Scriptures say not to test the Lord your God."

Then Satan showed Jesus all the castles and far kingdoms of the world. "If You worship me," he said, "I will give all these kingdoms to You."

"Go away, Satan!" Jesus said. "The Scriptures say to worship God only."

Satan left Jesus alone. Then angels came to take care of Jesus, for He was weak and hungry.

JESUS BEGINS HIS MINISTRY
The First Disciples

John 1:35-49

Two men who had been learning from John the Baptist heard John say that Jesus was the Lamb of God. They followed Jesus until He turned and said, "What do you want to know?" They spent that day with Him.

One of these men was Andrew. Andrew found his brother. "Simon, we have found the Messiah! Come, Simon, and we will take you to Him."

Simon did not know what to think, but when Jesus saw him, He said, "You are Simon, the son of John. You shall be called Cephas." The names Cephas and Peter both mean "rock." This was the first time Jesus met Peter.

The next day Jesus planned to go into Galilee. There he saw a man called Philip. "Follow me," he said, and Philip did so.

Philip went to a friend called Nathanael and said, "We have found the one Moses and the prophets spoke about. It is Jesus from Nazareth!"

Nathanael laughed and said he did not think there were any good people in Nazareth. But when he actually met Jesus, Jesus said, "I know you were sitting under a fig tree, thinking, when Philip called you."

Nathanael was amazed that Jesus would know what he had been doing, even though Jesus had not been anywhere near Nathanael at the time.

Nathanael said, "I believe. You are the Son of God. You are the King of Israel."

Jesus smiled. "Do you believe so easily? I tell you, you shall see greater things than these."

How to Catch Fish

Matthew 4:18-22; Mark 1:16-20; Luke 5:4-11

After Andrew brought Simon to meet Jesus, the two brothers returned home. They were fishermen and needed to take care of their boats and keep their nets mended in order to make a living. One day Jesus got into one of Simon's

boats, and asked him to pull out a little way from the land. He sat down in the boat and began teaching the crowd on the shore.

When Jesus finished speaking, He turned to Simon. "Go out into the deep water and let down your nets for a catch."

Simon said, "Teacher, we worked hard all night and caught nothing, but all right, I will do as You say."

When Peter dropped his net overboard and started to haul it in again he got the surprise of his life. It was full to the bursting point! He called another boat to come and help him. By the time he and the other men had hauled all the fish on board, both boats were ready to sink.

Peter was filled with amazement. He fell down at Jesus' feet and said, "Oh, please go away from me. I am a terrible man, and You are the Lord. I am so ashamed!"

But Jesus said to him and Andrew, "Don't be afraid. Follow me and I will help you become fishers of men." Peter and Andrew put down their nets, landed their boats, and followed Jesus.

As they walked along the shore, the little group soon met Simon's partners, two brothers named James and John. "Follow me," Jesus said. They put down their nets and walked after Jesus.

These men became Jesus' closest friends. They followed Him everywhere as He taught the people. They watched and learned from Him. They were Jesus' helpers, His first disciples.

"There's No More Wine!"

John 2:1-11

Jesus and His followers were invited to a wedding in Nathanael's hometown of Cana. It was a big wedding and the party lasted several days. Jesus' mother Mary was there, as well.

There were many, many people at the wedding. Food was heaped on tables. There was meat, nuts, rice, cakes, and fruit.

All the guests drank a great deal of wine, until partway through the feast when the bridegroom noticed the wine was running out. "Oh, no," he thought to himself. "This is the worst thing that can happen!" At Jewish weddings it was the bridegroom's job to make sure there was enough wine.

Mary saw the bridegroom's problem and went to Jesus. "They have no wine," she said.

Jesus said, "Do you think I should do something about it now?"

Mary called a servant and told him to do whatever Jesus ordered. Jesus told the servant to fill six huge jars with water.

"Take out some water now and bring it to the headwaiter," He said when the jars were full. The servant did so. When the headwaiter tasted the wine, he went to the bridegroom.

"What have you done?" he asked him. "This is the best wine I have ever tasted!" The bridegroom did not understand where all the wine had come from, but Mary knew.

This was the very first miracle Jesus did as a sign. A miracle is something that seems imposible that God makes happen. Jesus did miracles to help people in need and to show that God was with Him in a very special way.

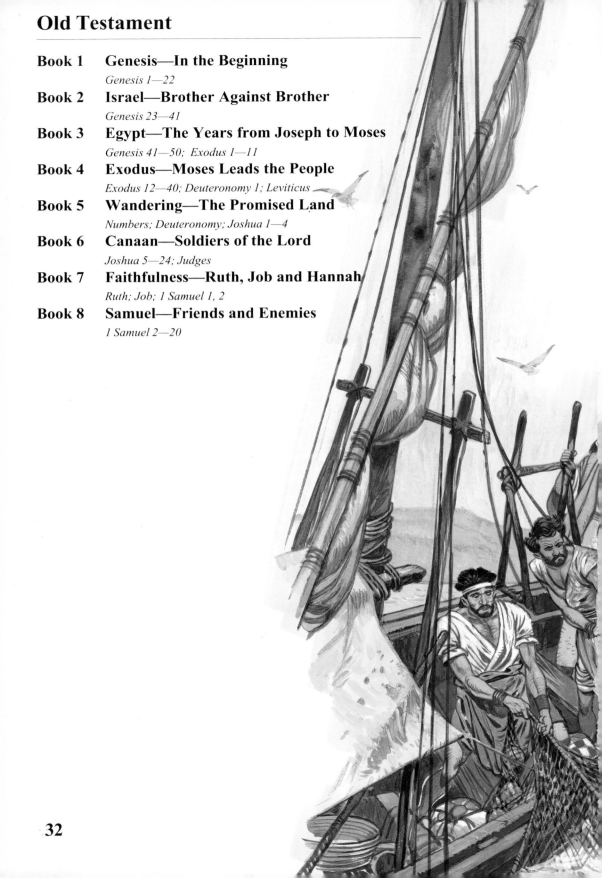

Old Testament

New Testament